A Parent's Guide to

Misophonia

Understanding and Managing

Misophonia

Regulate, Reason, Reassure

by Dr. Jennifer Jo Brout

The International Misophonia Research Network (IMRN)

Cover art and print/ebook design
by East Coast Designs
www.eastcoastdesigns.ca

Edited by Allison Weinig, Ann Marie Cunningham and
Macie Gardner
Copy Edited by Kerri Tolan

Print ISBN 978-1-7772632-9-4

Acknowledgments

I would like to thank the following friends, family, and colleagues for their help and inspiration regarding this manual and for their willingness to explore how sensory processing affects human behavior.

Dr. Roianne Ahn, Madeline Appelbaum, Madeline, Emily, and Bo Brout, Ameya Calvocoressi, Ann Marie Cunningham, Mercede Erfanian, Dr. Pawel Jastreboff, Lisalynn Kelly, Dr. Sukhbinder Kumar, Dr. Michael Mannino, Dr. Clair Robbins, Tim Sommer, and all of the staff at Duke CMER.

I extend a special thank you to Shaylynn Hayes for her partnership in advocating for misophonia, for her tireless work for this disorder, for her varied passions and talents, and for her friendship throughout this journey.

I would like to extend a special acknowledgement to three innovators who fundamentally shaped my thinking about and approach to the mystery of human behavior and who I am proud to also call colleagues and dear friends: Dr. Jooeph E. LeDoux, Dr. Lucy Jane Miller, and Dr. M. Zachary Rosenthal.

Table of Contents

Introduction

What Is Misophonia?

Research on misophonia is in the early stages, and therefore, the prevailing definition of the disorder is subject to change. Misophonia has been described as a neurologically based disorder characterized by heightened nervous system reactivity (e.g. irritation, anger, and anxiety) in response to a decreased tolerance for specific sounds (Brout et al., 2018; Cavanna & Seri, 2015).

Early research suggests that the brains of people with misophonia behave differently than others (Kumar et al., 2017; Schröder et al., 2019). Images of neural function demonstrate that when an individual with misophonia is exposed to certain sounds, there is increased activation and connectivity in brain areas associated with fight–flight, emotional processing, and unconsciously mediated auditory and visual attention. This means that an individual with misophonia will experience the physiological symptoms associated with fight–flight such as sweating, increased heartbeat, and hormonal changes, alongside cognitive and emotional changes when faced with auditory and visual triggers.

More recently, research informs us that the motor system is also involved in misophonia. Specifically, Kumar et al. (2021) used fMRI studies to demonstrate that there is connectivity between the auditory and orofacial motor cortices (Kumar et al., 18, 2021). From this new perspective, sounds are a 'medium' in which a motor action of the trigger sound or visual is "mirrored onto the listener." In other words, it is as if the individual with misophonia can *feel* in their own body that which they are hearing/seeing. What we are talking about here are mirror neurons. Kilner & Lemon (2013) explain the significance of mirror neurons:

Mirror neurons are a class of neuron that are activated both when an individual executes a specific motor act, and an individual observes a motor act performed by another… The discovery of motor neurons prompted the notion that, from a functional viewpoint, action execution and observation are closely related processes, and indeed that one's ability to interpret the actions of others requires the involvement of one's own motor system.

This research reframes our understanding of misophonia to include motor processing and may also offer understanding as to why misophonia sounds often center around the mouth. These findings also reveal why exposure and cognitive behavioral therapies alone have not been successful treatments. Kumar et al. (2021) suggests that "effective therapies should target the brain representation of movement" (Kumar et al., 3, 2021). Until there are more specific therapies, this coping skills approach serves to help parents assist their child work within multiple sensory-motor modalities to affect change.

While the Kumar et al. (2021) study tells us that sounds represent the action-oriented motor mirroring, we are still dealing with sounds (and visual stimuli) as the conduit of that action. Similarly, while we don't yet know how the mirror neuron hypothesis will affect treatment, we do know that the key to coping is learning how to de-escalate the nervous system.

The 3 Rs: What is Regulate, Reason, Reassure (RRR)?

Regulate, Reason, Reassure (RRR) is a coping-skills approach for parents to help their misophonic child cope with the everyday struggles of the disorder on their own or with the guidance of a therapist. RRR can be tailored for different aged children and adolescents. Older adolescents are often able to use RRR with greater independence.

RRR draws on principles from multiple cross-disciplinary therapies and prioritizes psychoeducation, which entails providing education and information to others to help them understand a disorder or condition. Psychoeducation in misophonia also involves assisting parents to better understand how to access help and advocate for their child.

In the case of misophonia, knowledge is power; understanding misophonia helps take the power out of the disorder.

Regulate

Regulation refers to the ability to independently calm when the nervous system is overstimulated. We refer to this as _self-_

regulation or *habituation*. Habituation occurs when the nervous system returns to its neutral state or homeostasis. With misophonia, we are dealing with a neurological response that sets off a cascade of physiological, cognitive, and emotional changes. Although the neurological response comes first and the other changes occur within milliseconds, all of these changes feel as though they are happening simultaneously and are outside of the individual's awareness (LeDoux & Brown, 2017). These changes are negative, overwhelming, and frightening for a child to experience.

This reaction is part of our neurophysiological defense response and is mediated by a part of the brain called the *amygdala* (LeDoux, 2012). Neurological response to outside stimuli sets off this physiological, emotional, and cognitive cascade, yet we talk about it in misophonia as if it were one event. Therefore, it is very important to begin by helping your child parse out these different facets of this complex response.

Most people run into difficulty differentiating emotions from the rest of the multifaceted defense response. Consider what emotions are. Are emotions simply consequences of our physiological reactions? Neuroscientist Dr. Joseph LeDoux (2015) says this is too simple of an explanation.

Here is how LeDoux described an emotion:

"An emotion is an aggregate of many neural, physiological, and cognitive systems" — *J. E. LeDoux (personal communication, 2015).*

There is no consensus as to where physiology ends, and emotions begin. Thus, it is somewhat of an art to understand and portray these distinct, yet interrelated dimensions of the misophonic reaction to your child. I hope as you continue to read, these distinctions will become clearer.

How Self-Regulation Skills Develop

Although we do not know how or when misophonia actually begins, we do know that most children start developing the long journey toward self-regulation in infancy. An individual develops the ability to _self-regulate_ through interactions with caregivers. This period is characterized by the infant's desire to be near the primary caregiver, the instinct to return to the caregiver when in danger, and dependence on the caregiver as a "secure base" from which to explore the world (Bowlby, 1958). The infant seeks proximity to their caregiver because the infant needs the caregiver's help to regulate when distressed. When a caregiver assists an infant to calm, this is referred to as _co-regulation_.

Self-regulation abilities typically increase as a child ages. However, like a distressed infant, a child or adolescent with misophonia has great difficulty self-regulating. Does this mean that you have to pick up and rock or swaddle your 10-year-old? No, it does not. However, we can use (or help our children to learn how to use) different applications of physiological and sensory-based principles underlying what we naturally do with infants.

To summarize, children, adolescents, and even adults with misophonia have difficulty with the physiological, emotional, and cognitive elements required to facilitate self-regulation and need help from their caregivers.

Self-Regulation and Self-Control

It is also essential to distinguish self-regulation from self-control; they are not the same (Shanker & Barker, 2017). Self-control refers to refraining from unwanted behaviors through willpower. Self-regulation, on the other hand, refers to the ability to use one's own physiological, cognitive, and emotional resources to keep the body and mind at a low level of stress or to lower one's overall stress level.

Self-regulating in the face of a trigger sound or visual stimulus is highly challenging by the almost-immediate neurophysiologic response that causes a child to feel out of control. Willpower is not the antidote to misophonia. Instead, supporting your child's acquisition of self-regulation skills is key.

Coping with misophonia is not about willpower or choice. Willpower is not the antidote to misophonic reactivity; self-regulation is.

Bottom-Up and Top-Down Processing

Another way to explain the RRR coping-skills approach has to do with *bottom-up* and *top-down* processing. Some therapies are, by nature, physiological and/or sensory-based, and others are cognitive and/or behavior-based. Some therapies attempt to integrate these different approaches. Given that we are dealing with a millisecond response driven by the brain and experienced through our thoughts and our emotions, we need to engage both a bottom-up and top-down approach to self-regulation. Bottom-up processing, in this context, includes using physical activities to help integrate the senses and impact nervous system arousal. Top-down processing refers to using cognition to affect change. For example, one may try replacing negative thoughts with positive ones to affect the physiological state.

It is evident that using both top-down and bottom-up approaches to self-regulate and treat misophonia is necessary. For example, Kumar et al. (2017) found that individuals with misophonia have differences in _interoception_. Interoception refers to an awareness of our internal body states and functions. Kumar et al. (2017) hypothesized that the difficulty in processing sensory information in these brain networks leads to a mismatch between how a person perceives their physical state and what their physical state really is.

RRR strives to help you guide your child toward an awareness of these different but interacting facets of self-regulation. RRR also enables your child to become less overwhelmed when facing triggering sounds or visuals.

Reason

Reasoning more specifically addresses the cognitive shifts, or thoughts, that occur in response to trigger sounds and visual stimuli. It may help to think about a time that _you_ have felt highly dysregulated. It is often difficult to think clearly, isn't it?

The same is true in misophonia. Because the neurological response happens so quickly, it is difficult to access cognition, much less utilize thoughts to self-regulate.

Reasoning takes many forms, both in the moment and over time. Reasoning helps your child build an awareness of misophonia triggers as well as the neurophysiological, cognitive, and emotional mechanisms of misophonia. Reasoning also helps your child to build a toolbox to cope with triggers and triggering situations, develop and maintain self-esteem and social relationships, and enjoy the world.

Reassure

The last R is perhaps more intuitive, but is just as important as the first two Rs. Building coping skills is not easy for your child, and it is not easy for a parent. Many children with misophonia describe themselves as being *taken over* by bad feelings and sensations. They have even referred to themselves as becoming *monsters* during a misophonic reaction. The way in which an individual views the self while experiencing a misophonic reaction is at odds with how one views the self holistically. This unintentional view can easily impact one's identity and self-esteem.

In psychology, there is a useful, albeit somewhat outdated, term, _ego-dystonic_, which explains how people feel when aspects of their self-image do not align with their overall self-concept. _Ego-syntonic_, on the other hand, refers to ideas, thoughts, and emotions that are in line with one's self-concept. For many people suffering from misophonia, the way they feel when reacting to sounds and visuals is ego-dystonic. The person they feel they become when triggered does not match who they feel they truly are. This is emotionally painful and makes people with misophonia doubt who they are. This is where reassurance comes in.

In addition, there will inevitably be times of frustration and times in which you and your child feel as though you are going one step forward and two steps backward. With this in mind, it is important to remember to reassure your child, yourself, and other family members that things are going to get better.

Summary

Although the physiological, cognitive, and emotional responsivity to sounds and visual stimuli feel as though they occur simultaneously, it is important to assist your child in breaking up the larger experience into more manageable parts.

Even if a child cannot control the reactivity at first, continuing to work on these differentiations is an essential first step. By using both top-down and bottom-up self-regulation skills training, the individual comes to feel more empowered and less overwhelmed. This is especially important for the misophonic child because negative reactivity, coupled with a lack of understanding of one's own responses, only creates more negative physiological and emotional arousal.

Next, we will look more closely at the history of misophonia as well as the ways in which misinformation has been inadvertently absorbed by the press and even within academic work. We will also dive into some of the early research and clinical observation regarding misophonia and co-occurring disorders. I hope you will emerge from the next section with a clearer understanding of what misophonia is and what it is not.

1. Defining Misophonia

The Dominos of Disbelief

To thoroughly understand a new disorder, it helps to review its history. Without attention to its history, the medical community often regards a newly proposed condition as unreal because descriptions have been haphazardly built out of ambiguous bits of information that ultimately don't add up to anything grounded in theory. Until recently, almost every academic or popular press article about misophonia began like this:

"Misophonia, which means hatred of sound, was termed by Jastreboff and Jastreboff in 2001."

After this cursory mention of the Jastreboffs and their role in naming misophonia, authors often jump to their own interpretations. Misophonia has, unfortunately, fallen victim to this phenomenon, which I call "the dominos of disbelief."

To help put together the puzzle pieces of misophonia, let's begin with the original conception of the disorder. While working in their audiology clinic, the Jastreboffs observed that some people reacted to sounds such as chewing, pencil tapping, keyboard typing, and coughing with levels of irritability ranging from moderate to extreme (Brout et al., 2018).

Unlike their patients with *hyperacusis*, a disorder in which people perceive sounds more loudly than objectively measured, the Jastreboffs noticed that individuals with misophonia appeared to respond to pattern-based sounds with autonomic nervous system arousal. That is, upon presentation of such stimuli, patients reported rising stress levels such as elevated heartbeat, muscle tension, and sweating along with strong, negative emotions. This was different from what the Jastreboffs had seen regarding other forms of "decreased sound tolerance" (Jastreboff & Jastreboff, 2001) such as *tinnitus*, which is ringing in one or both ears, and *phonophobia*, which is the fear of sound often secondary to hyperacusis.

Taking this a step back, think about how we should

conceptualize misophonia based on its origins. Although the Jastreboffs suggested that misophonia involves negative associations between auditory, cognitive, and emotional areas of the brain, they did not view misophonia as a *psychiatric disorder* (personal communication, 2015). In the past few years, research has clarified that misophonia is a disorder that crosses the boundaries of disciplines (Brout et al., 2018). For this reason, coping skills are based on multidisciplinary research and treatment and take into consideration movement as a way to self-regulate.

What Is a Trigger Sound?

The sounds that the misophonic finds highly aversive are known as *trigger sounds*. Across early studies, symptoms reported by individuals with misophonia vary. Also, across studies, there is a striking similarity between the sounds typically considered triggering. While Jastreboff and Jastreboff (2001) mentioned "pattern-based sounds," repetitive sounds are also an issue (Brout et al., 2018). Notably, the Jastreboffs (2001) did not suggest that these sounds were primarily mouth sounds or even necessarily generated by other human beings. Yet Kumar et al.'s (2021) paper in which the orofacial motor cortices are involved supports the idea that people/mouth sounds may be more severe triggers for those with misophonia. However, we must keep in mind that many also report difficulty with nonorganic sounds such as windshield wipers, car turn signals, and keyboard or pencil tapping (Brout et al., 2018). As research continues, we hope to find these answers.

It is most important to note that triggers are not 'contagious'. Many parents, older children, and adolescents express worry that talking about triggers will result in a worsening of reactivity—or hearing about triggers will result in an increase in the number of triggering sounds. This simply is not true. Triggers seem to increase during a short period of time after the individual initially becomes aware of misophonia. Similarly, misophonia waxes and wanes. When your child isn't feeling well or is poorly rested, misophonia reactivity may become worse. Yet, it will likely go back to baseline when your child feels better.

Therefore, it is best not to focus on trigger sounds as separate entities but to instead focus on how your child reacts to triggers and how you can help. Especially in light of Kumar et al.'s (2021) research in which we know the motor cortex is involved in misophonia, focusing on the trigger sounds rather than how to de-escalate the neurophysiological response may not be prudent. Rather, focus on self-regulation.

What About Visual Triggers?

Schröder et al. (2013) suggested the term *misokinesia* to describe a phenomenon in which individuals experience an aversive response to repetitive visual stimuli or movement. For example, the sight of another person jiggling their leg, a common nervous habit, is frequently reported as a trigger. In view of Dr. Kumar's et al.'s (2021) work, we can see how misokinesia, as "hatred of movement," makes sense. If I see a person shaking their leg and I feel compelled to shake my leg, it is a very uncomfortable sensation that could easily make me feel a loss of physical agency. Notably, Kumar's et al.'s (2021) paper describes findings related to the orofacial motor cortex, whereas Schröder's description, as well as clinical observation, suggest other motor areas (e.g. gross motor areas may be involved). Again, we await more research to vet this out. Yet, we have so much more information than we did a few years ago!

Again, while the original meaning of misokinesia refers to aversive reactivity to another person's movement, many use the term to refer to any visual stimulus that causes negative reactivity. It is possible that there are two kinds of visual triggers: one related to another person's movement, or misokinesia and another related to memory association. That is, sounds may pair with visual stimuli in memory, thereby activating the same nervous system response.

Age of Onset

The age of onset of misophonia has been popularized in the press and reported in early academic research as occurring between 8 and 12 years of age. Yet, I have seen toddlers display symptoms. Unfortunately, research has not yet examined misophonia in very young children, and this leaves us at a loss in terms of diagnosis of these youngsters. However, research is gaining ground, and I look forward soon to studies that are focused on young children.

Gender

Initial case studies (e.g. Bernstein; Ferreira et al., 2013; Johnson et al., 2013; Kluckow et al., 2014; Neal & Cavanna, 2012; Webber et al., 2014) suggest that misophonia tends to occur at a higher rate in female compared to male individuals.

However, one should not make presumptions based on this early data as there may be other factors affecting this observation. For example, females have traditionally been more likely to seek help for medical and mental health–related issues. This finding may skew the gender ratio toward females. Like the age of onset, it is always better to wait until further data from research involving larger samples is studied.

Genetics

There has been one association of genes and misophonia. The company _23andMe_ identified one genetic marker associated with misophonia (i.e., rage associated with chewing). This genetic marker is located near the TENM2 gene, which is involved in brain development. The genetic marker associated with this trait is just one piece of the puzzle and does not mean that nongenetic factors do not also play a role (Center for Disease Control, 2020). Today geneticists think beyond the binary nature-versus-nurture terms. Instead, they think genes may be "turned on or turned off" based on environmental events. Thus, geneticists now think in terms of nature via nurture (Pizzi, 2004). The study of the process by which certain genes can be turned on within individuals is called _epigenetics._

Likely then, misophonia is a combination of genetic and environmental influences.

Co-Occurring Disorders

Misophonia is most likely a distinct disorder that is not better explained by the symptoms of any other disorder. However, the symptoms of misophonia are associated with other disorders and may also co-occur with other conditions. Note, there is a distinct difference between co-occurrences and symptom overlaps. When disorders co-occur, this means that an individual meets the criterion for one or more disorders. When symptoms overlap, the individual usually meets the criterion for one disorder and not a second, yet the individual still has symptoms of both.

Both anecdotal observations and empirical findings in the audiology field suggest that there is a higher incidence of misophonia among individuals with tinnitus and/or hyperacusis (Baguley et al., 2016). In the mental health realm, we have seen misophonia and its symptoms co-occur with anxiety, *obsessive-compulsive personality disorder (OCPD)*, *sensory processing disorder (SPD)*, and *autistic spectrum disorder (ASD)*. However, these co-occurrences and symptom overlaps must be viewed with caution. There is a long way to go before any of these associations are understood scientifically. Yet, these possibilities are good to keep in mind due to their implications for your child's experience of misophonia, diagnosis, and coping-skills development.

These associations, which often cross the boundaries of disciplines, are also one of the best justifications for multidisciplinary research, diagnosis and treatment. Unfortunately, parents ultimately end up being the case manager for their child's team of professionals. Although this is difficult for parents, getting to know what kinds of practitioners are available can ease this stressor.

Summary

As is true of most newly termed disorders, early studies can be misleading as research begins with hypotheses. Early research is often not funded, and therefore, only small samples or case studies are possible. Regarding misophonia, the press picked up on some misinformation quite early, making for a highly confusing picture of what the disorder is. Over the past five years, more stringent research has come into play, and we can more easily identify and dispel some of the common myths.

Misophonia is not simply rage in response to chewing. As the Jastreboffs originally suggested, adverse reactivity occurs in response to a variety of patterned-based sounds—some people-centric, others nonorganic. Misophonia may co-occur with other auditory, psychological, and possibly health-related disorders, but it should not be considered a psychiatric disorder. The relationship of age and gender to misophonia is still anecdotal, and genetic work is in the very early stages. However, research is ongoing, and I am hopeful that answers to all of our questions are soon forthcoming.

In the next section, I discuss the different kinds of doctors and therapists who can help your child, what characteristics to look for in a clinician, and the typical trials and tribulations parents experience as they are faced with managing their child's care.

2. Who Can Help My Child?

Case Management

While parents often end up struggling to manage their child's care, they also inadvertently open themselves up to criticism. I am sure many of you have experienced this. You are *pushy parents*. You are the *annoying parents* or the *helicopter parents*. I experienced this despite being a psychologist, and it was both painful and frustrating

As mothers, we also fall victim to mother blaming and sexism. How many of you have been told that you are making your child's problems worse? How many moms out there have been called *dramatic*? We also run into victim-blaming tactics aimed at our suffering child. How many of you have heard something like, "Your child is using this to get attention?" These remarks, whether delivered with malintent or simply inconsideration, are hurtful.

As an aside, my then 16-year-old daughter once said, "Who would make up [a condition] where sounds bother you… I mean, who would think to come up with that ruse?" And she was right. What child is going to make up the story of misophonia? What is the end game—to control the family via the dinner table?

Although there is no elixir for this, there are steps parents can take to minimize the impact of these experiences. Refrain from being defensive if you can, and instead, provide information. A true professional will admit what they don't know without being dismissive or critical and will welcome information. So, when you visit clinicians and doctors, be armed with information.

Multidisciplinary Professionals

The following is a list of multidisciplinary professionals for your reference:

Pediatricians or Adolescent Health Doctors

Research in terms of misophonia and medical disorders is very sparse, but there are some speculative overlaps. Therefore, it is always a good idea to have a physician rule out any underlying medical conditions. Beyond a routine medical evaluation, pediatricians may want to test for conditions such as tick-borne illnesses and may want to perform an endocrine panel for hormonal issues. In doing so, they may identify and recommend treatment for medical problems that may produce symptoms akin to misophonia and/or worsen misophonia symptoms.

Audiologists

Audiologists assist children with misophonia by introducing sound generators or special apps to mask certain sounds and/or generate white noise or other kinds of noises based on frequency. Devices such as these may mask trigger sounds while still allowing the individual to hear and participate in conversations. With these devices, audiologists may provide individuals the means to reduce their sensitivity to aversive sounds. I always suggest seeing an audiologist first or an _ear–nose–throat (ENT) doctor_ to rule out any anatomical issues with the ear or other auditory disorders.

Occupational Therapists

Physiological or sensory-based occupational therapies are those that directly affect the nervous system. A simple breathing technique is a form of physiological therapy. Occupational therapists (OT's) are specially trained to work with the sensory systems that are intertwined with the nervous system. They are also excellent clinicians when it comes to working with children with numerous disorders that include self-regulation difficulties. There are some general ways that help people self-regulate. Yet, each child is individual in the specific ways sensation may be used to assist calming the system, and OTs are unique in their training to do this.

Individual Therapists and Counselors

Individual therapy and supportive counseling can be beneficial for anyone in distress. It is helpful to know that psychologists and counselors have many different approaches and work from various schools of thought. The theoretical grounding and different types of therapists and counselors available is extensive. Knowing what is right for your child may be very confusing given all these options. Some psychologists are trained in active methods to bring about change. This would include, for example, the numerous forms of cognitive or behavior-based therapy such as *cognitive behavior therapy (CBT) and dialectical behavior therapy* (DBT; American Psychological Association, 2017). In the glossary you will see other forms of cognitive based therapies such as *Acceptance and Commitment Therapy* (ACT), and you have also probably heard of mindfulness training. The take home message here is that CBT is not one therapy but is many different therapies. For a comprehensive list of CBT approaches and techniques see www.infocounselling.com/list-of-cbt-techniques.

Others, such as counselors trained in supportive methods, prioritize listening empathetically. Some clinicians work from an eclectic approach, incorporating techniques from multiple theoretical groundings.

Psychiatrists

While there is no medically approved treatment for misophonia, psychiatrists may assist in parsing out and treating comorbid conditions. It is helpful to address comorbid conditions, if possible, therefore making it easier for the patient to cope with misophonia.

Psychiatrists may also suggest treating symptoms by using off-label medications for their misophonic patients. Again, it is imperative that any medical doctor explain their rationale for doing so and make sure the patient knows that this is experimental (and, of course, understands the risks). Currently, there are no rigorous studies regarding misophonia and medication.

Family Therapists

When we are dealing with a child with misophonia, the entire family is impacted. Given that, family therapists can be of great value in the face of the specific familial challenges (Shadish & Baldwin, 2003). There are numerous schools of thought in terms of practicing family therapy. I find that a family systems approach is best for misophonia.

Psychiatrist Murray Bowen, M.D., was one of the pioneers of family systems therapy. Dr. Bowen noted that positive changes in one family member changed the way everyone else functioned (The Bowen Center for the Study of the Family, n.d.). The changes that took place did not necessarily occur first within the family member identified as the patient. Considering this observation, Dr. Bowen maintained that the family, not the patient, should be the focus of treatment. The value of the systems approach is that when one person in the family makes a positive change, even if it is not the identified patient, the system changes for the better.

Biofeedback Practitioners

These practitioners use biofeedback along with guided imagery and other relaxation techniques or distractive methods to affect physiological change. During a biofeedback session, one can see their stress responses on a monitor in real time and may use various cognitive and physiologically based relaxation techniques to learn how to improve reactivity to triggers.

While some people have found biofeedback anecdotally helpful, there are few studies supporting change and/or lasting change. Another issue with biofeedback is that it may be difficult for the individual to transfer what they have learned during biofeedback sessions into the moment of misophonic responding.

Biofeedback can be helpful as an adjunct to other coping skills methods. However, there is no evidence that biofeedback is, on its own, a form of therapy for misophonia.

Neurofeedback Practitioners

Neurofeedback is similar to biofeedback. However, rather than attaching sensors to the body to monitor heart rate, _electroencephalogram (EEG)_ sensors are attached to the scalp to monitor brain activities. In a neurofeedback practitioner's office, one will see their brain waves appear on a monitor in the form of a game. The goal is to alter one's brain waves to a more adaptive pattern. Again, it is up to the individual to use physiological and cognitive skills to affect change. Notably, brain waves are only one small facet of understanding the exceedingly complex functioning of the brain. Biofeedback and neurofeedback can certainly be helpful as part of a multidisciplinary coping skills plan. However, neither are a cure for misophonia.

Summary

It can be frustrating for a parent to figure out who can help their child, which is how and why RRR was developed. From my experience, a parent is their child's best advocate, and coping skills training works well alongside a clinician who is willing to be a partner in this process. The following is a list of practitioner traits that I feel are most important:

- Knowledge of misophonia and/or willingness to learn about misophonia from professional workshops, forums, and peer-reviewed papers.
- A willingness to reach out to multi-disciplinary practitioners that may also be able to work on your child's team.
- Respect for your concerns about your child and a willingness to consider your personal parenting values.
- Flexibility. Since we are in new territory with misophonia, flexibility is highly important. If something the therapist is doing is not working or is negatively impacting your child, it is the therapist's job to address this and find other ways to proceed or make a referral to another clinician.

As we move into the next section, we will dig deeper into how misophonia affects your child's body. A review of the basics of the nervous system will help you understand what your child is up against and how you can assist toward better self-regulation. This next section may be a little weighty, but don't feel discouraged and feel free to take it slowly. I didn't have a background in any of this when I was a young parent either, and I'm still learning.

3. Understanding Your Child's Body

Understanding neurophysiological systems will allow you to better understand your child's behavior and better promote your child's self-regulation. In addition, understanding the mechanisms that underlie misophonia more thoroughly will reassure you that you are not failing as a parent. This is a difficult disorder to understand and one that engenders a high level of frustration for both children and their parents. Although this text has referenced the nervous system generally, we will dig deeper into the functioning of the *autonomic nervous system (ANS)*.

The ANS is one major part of the nervous system that

controls the involuntary response of many organs and muscles. In most situations, we are unaware of the ANS' functioning because its actions are unconscious, thereby requiring no thought or effort (Low, 2020). The ANS contains the _sympathetic_, _parasympathetic,_ and _enteric nervous system_. For purposes of misophonia, we will concentrate on the sympathetic and parasympathetic nervous system.[1]

The Sympathetic Nervous System

One of the sympathetic nervous system's primary functions is to stimulate the body's fight–flight response. This physiological reaction occurs when one perceives a threat. The defense response, which is an updated term inclusive of the fight–flight reaction, enables one to fight or to escape a dire situation quickly by flooding the body with hormones that provide increased energy (Low, 2020). Even though the terms "sympathetic nervous system arousal" and "fight–flight" are

---

[1] The enteric nervous system exerts a profound influence on all digestive processes, namely motility, ion transport, and gastrointestinal blood flow. Some of this control emanates from connections between the digestive system and central nervous system (Bowen, n.d.). For further information see
http://www.vivo.colostate.edu/hbooks/pathphys/digestion/basics/gi_nervous.html

interchangeable in this text, it is important to take a moment to point out how they are different. Sympathetic arousal refers to an escalation of the sympathetic nervous system, and fight–flight is the extreme end of this escalation.

The defense response can sometimes be activated by what some people call irrational fears or phobias. Here, the defense response is activated when it is not needed in situations that mimic threat (Ledoux, 2003). Often these irrational fears are cognitively motivated. *I am worried about school grades* (thought) and my sympathetic system is activated. *I fear spiders*, thus, when I see one, I experience sympathetic system changes.

Sympathetic arousal in response to worry or anxiety may be stimulated by internal stimuli such as thoughts. In misophonia, sympathetic arousal is a direct result of outside stimuli. That is, a sound or a visual stimulus from the outside world kicks off the defense response. This is a very important distinction, setting misophonia apart from other disorders that one might consider more psychological in nature.

The Parasympathetic Nervous System

The body's attempt to combat this reaction and return to homeostasis or calm involves the other part of the ANS. The parasympathetic nervous system puts on the brakes to return the body to homeostasis or neutral (Low, 2020). This is called _habituation_. Habituation is highly intertwined with self-regulation.

Sympathetic	Parasympathetic
System known to be responsible for arousal that leads to fight–flight response	Puts the brakes on fight–flight response (also known as the "digest and rest" system)
Automatically set into action when outside stimuli cue that the organism may be under threat	Set into action when person has reached safety or assesses situational danger to be false
Adrenaline released and blood flow directed to major muscles	Acetylcholine released
Blood pressure increases	Lowers blood pressure and aids digestion
Heart rate increases	Heart rate decreases

Table 1. The Autonomic Nervous System (sympathetic and parasympathetic)

Alerting, Arousal, and Attention

The brain's innate ability to alert us to auditory and other sensory stimuli is essential to survival. Prior to experiencing nervous system arousal, we must be alert to stimuli. Think how we rely on our sense of smell to alert us to the potential danger of something. For example, we smell something burning and we think, "fire."

Alerting often occurs outside of, or before, the individual's awareness. Unbeknownst to us, our brains are always scanning our surroundings via our senses to know when and where to focus attention. This is known as _pre-attention_. Pre-attention, then, is not something we control. Rather, it is an unconscious process preserved by evolution that allows us to know when we are in danger (LeDoux, 2015).

Many parents ask me why their child stares at triggering sounds or visuals. This is pre-attention at work. Second, think about how you would react if a dangerous animal suddenly appeared in your room. Would you take your eyes off it? I am sure you would not. In a sense, misophonia triggers are like dangerous animals. One's brain _knows_ to pay attention. The most useful way to override the brain's natural attentional processes is to focus on one's physiological response and gain insight into how one's body reacts to sympathetic nervous system arousal.

Now that we have covered alerting and attention, let us think more deeply about arousal.[2] Sympathetic nervous system arousal can range from very low to very high. We have all been in low arousal states and high arousal states as well as everything in between. Right now, try to use yourself as an example.

For a moment, do not think about your emotions or thoughts. Just think about yourself in terms of your physical state. What are you doing, and how does your body feel right now? Are you reading in bed? Are you sitting up in a chair? Is your heart rate fast or normal? Are you falling asleep? Would you say your body state is calm and alert, or are you distracted?

Now that you have focused on your body, you hopefully have an idea of what arousal is. When arousal is low, you can be slow, sluggish, calm, non-reactive, or asleep. When arousal is very high, you are extremely alert. Conceptually, arousal stands on its own and describes the *intensity* of a response. However,

---

[2] For the purposes of this text, arousal and sympathetic arousal are interchangeable terms.

to truly make sense of one's physiological state, one must also think about _valence_, which is the qualifier for arousal.

What Is the Difference between Arousal and Valence?

The terms arousal and valence describe two separate states of mind and body. Valence tells us if one's arousal level (whatever the intensity) is positive or negative. The important idea to remember is that arousal can be high when valence is low and vice versa. For a visual representation, see _Table 2 below._

Arousal	Valence	Result
High	Positive	Happy, excited
Low	Negative	Depressed, sad, bored
High	Negative	Frightened, anxious, angry
Low	Positive	Calm, complacent, satisfied, relaxed

Table 2. Arousal and Valence

Summary

Children and adolescents with misophonia experience high arousal coupled with negative valence intermittently throughout each day and are subjected to continual dysregulation. For parents, knowledge of arousal and valence is key. Once parents realize what is going on inside their child's body and mind, they can begin to help their children parse out what is happening to them.

Now that you have an idea about the underlying neurophysiological and auditory mechanisms that underlie misophonia, you will be better equipped to help your child. Again, don't feel overwhelmed if you found the last section a bit dense. As you will see, the next part addresses the sensory strategies that we use to lower sympathetic nervous system arousal. Read on and the practice of RRR comes together!

4. Applying RRR Principles/Sensory Strategies

As we go through the next sections, we will apply the specific principles of RRR including the use of sensory-based and other physiological strategies. We will then discuss how to integrate cognitive and practical strategies in the following sections. In addition, we will cover strategies that can assist with the stressors misophonia causes within the family. We begin with the sensory–physiological because we abide by the idea of physiological regulating before cognitive. I provide worksheets presented in example form, and you will find the full worksheets (as well as reminders sheets) at the end of the manual.

Be Sensible (Reminder Sheet #1)

We all know that certain activities are naturally calming. Some of these activities refer to what we do with babies (i.e., rocking, swaddling, patting the baby gently on the back, etc.). We may also refer to these as sensory-based activities because they focus on ways to use our child's sensory preferences to self-regulate. Most of us know that we have the following five senses:

- **Sight** (Vision)
- **Hearing** (Auditory)
- **Smell** (Olfactory)
- **Taste** (Gustatory)
- **Touch** (Tactile)

However, the classic list of senses continues past common knowledge and includes the following three often-overlooked senses:

- **Interoception** (what we feel inside our bodies)
- **Vestibular** (sense of balance and rotation)
- **Proprioception** (sense of where our bodies are in space, understood through input to our muscles and joints)

Interoception is the intensity with which we feel our body's internal functions. Since we know that Kumar et al. (2017) found differences in the interoceptive sense in individuals with misophonia, it follows that we include this in our investigation of our own and our child's perception of the world.

Next, the _vestibular_ sense is related to balance and body rotation. The connection between the vestibular sense and misophonia has not been established but is also worth exploring because the vestibular sense is connected to the middle ear. In fact, the vestibular sense resides in sense organs called cilia, which are little hairs deep within the ear that send out signals to the auditory nerve (Mailloux & Smith, 2013).

Finally, we must also consider the sense of _proprioception_. Proprioception tells us how and where our bodies are in space by using external sensory input to our muscles and joints. Many people find proprioceptive input to be quickly and intensely calming. Think, for example, of how many people enjoy yoga, stretching, and massage—all proprioceptive activities.

Why Use Calming Sensory-Based Activities?

There are three ways to use sensory-based activities for misophonia management. The first way is to keep general sympathetic system arousal low during everyday life. These activities are important to incorporate into your child's daily schedule. The second way is to use calming activities to bring down arousal when your child is going into a triggering situation. These activities are generally the same as the everyday ones, however, you are using them proactively. The third way is to translate these activities into ones that may be used in the *misophonia moment*. This is the tricky part.

Although none of these activities are a cure-all for misophonia, having them in a toolbox will help you help your child self-regulate. Depending on your child's age and developmental stage, you can assist with these activities and/or guide your child toward doing them independently. Don't get frustrated if your child needs your help for a while before self-regulation occurs. Remember, young children still rely on parents and other adults for physiological calming as do older children with misophonia. For more information, see the STAR Institute at sensoryhealth.org.

Keeping Arousal Low (Relaxing Activities and Everyday Practice)

We know, for example, that taking a bath is calming for many of us. While bathing, we are using our tactile sense (touch) as we feel the warm water against our skin. We are also enjoying proprioceptive input (to our muscles and joints) as the pressure of the water surrounds us. Many of us find rocking chairs soothing. Here, we see rocking as a utilization of the vestibular sense, de-escalating sympathetic nervous system reactivity. It is no wonder new parents use rockers and gliders to calm their infants. Similarly, swaddling, as a parent might do with an infant, calls upon the proprioceptive sense as baby enjoys pressure into the muscles and joints. The following list shows activities that we find naturally relaxing. After the list is an explanation of how the sensory system is utilized so that you can translate these ideas to your home.

Keeping Arousal Low at Home: Relaxing Activities/Everyday Practice (Worksheet #1)
Massage (foot rollers, hand rollers, etc.)
Rocking (or gliding) in chair
Rocking (or gliding) in chair with weighted blanket
Rolling on the floor or mat
Stretching
Taking a bath
Weighted blanket
Yoga

Massage: Most of us understand the relaxing quality of massage. The art of massage offers pain relief, relaxation, and has been around for centuries. There are even massage therapists who specialize in infant massage. However, on a more practical basis, we can use foot rollers, foam rollers, scalp massagers, and the like, which are all easily found on Amazon and other supplier websites. These devices, which are too extensive to list, can be used with your child. Again, we are using proprioceptive input (input to the muscles and joints) to bring in the parasympathetic system.

Rocking or gliding: Some children prefer rocking and others prefer gliding. Each uses the vestibular sense to bring in the parasympathetic system and help a child self-regulate. I wouldn't suggest purchasing a rocker or glider until you have had your child try both out. However, purchasing one and/or buying a slightly used one is often worthwhile as it can be used into adulthood. Most adults can probably relate to, or have even experienced, how rocking or gliding is soothing to a baby or to the self. Again, regardless of age, these sensory-based principles are the same.

Rolling: Rolling on the floor combines tactile, proprioceptive, and the vestibular senses. Some children may habituate more quickly if they roll back and forth quickly, and others may feel more at ease going slowly. Some children enjoy being wrapped in a blanket and rolled back and forth on the floor gently. This activity requires adult assistance and can be a wonderfully co-regulating experience for you and your child.

Weighted blanket: A weighted blanket uses the sense of proprioception to calm the nervous system. The amount of weight that a child needs to calm varies (Miller et al., 2009). It is okay to experiment with different weights with your child. Should you choose, rather than purchase an expensive weighted blanket, you can use heavy quilts and bedspreads instead. Combining the use of a weighted blanket and a rocker–glider is often very effective.

Stretching: Stretching also provides input to muscles and joints. In fact, stretching loosens tight muscles, and this helps the muscles relax. Stretching also increases blood flow to various areas of the body and triggers the brain to release natural chemicals (i.e. endorphins) that make the body feel tranquil.

Warm bath: A warm bath provides both tactile and proprioceptive input and generally brings in a sense of calm. To make the bath more comfortable, I suggest adding a bath pillow or fragrances such as a bath bomb. Many of these types of products are made organically and without chemicals and can be found online or in local shops. Finally, like adults, children may find lower light during bathing more soothing. Obviously, avoid the use of burning candles but rather use battery operated candles and/or light sources.

Yoga: Yoga is a combination of many of these activities and is also an excellent form of exercise depending on what level one practices. As yoga has become more and more popular, yoga for young children is available both at yoga studios, gyms, and online in the form of live and prerecorded classes. Yoga can also be a fun family activity and may also be an exercise program for adolescents. Many parents have told me that therapists have suggested meditation and/or muscle relaxation techniques. However, I find that it is very difficult for people with misophonia to meditate or use muscle relaxation techniques because we are always distracted by sound, and our bodies are always in overdrive. Yet, with the body moving in yoga, the senses work differently, the attention systems work differently, and success is achievable. Meditation is wonderful, but I have always said that it is for the very well-regulated. People with misophonia need more sensory input and more movement.

Other Sensible Activities

Walking Outside

The outdoors is also a wonderful place for children with misophonia—think simply of acoustics. If one is inside at a kitchen table, sound is not absorbed and is literally bouncing off the surrounding walls right back at your child. Outside, however, sound dissipates, which is why this is an effective activity. It is often a practical idea to use sound-absorbing materials in your home such as curtains, rugs, pillows, and so forth. Although this is not a cure-all, it can help a little, and a little goes a long way with misophonia.

A Place in the House

Make your child a special place in the house where they feel secure. This place in the home can have sensory-based activities and offer a calming environment in which children can go to help regulate. For example, children enjoy little tents and fortresses. This may seem like something only a very young child might like. However, older children and teenagers also often find solace in their own comforting space. Ask your child what they would like in their space. What do they find calming? Often, school-aged children like music, soft pillows, various kinds of squeeze toys and/or toys that engage the tactile and proprioceptive system. Teenagers may like similar items in their space and may also enjoy books, music, or calming videos.

Listening to Music

Music can be an excellent source of relaxation even for those with misophonia. As I think we now know, people with misophonia don't hate sound itself, rather they are averse to very specific kinds of sounds. Enjoying music, however, isn't as simple as listening to what is typically thought of as calming. The body of work in music neuroscience and music therapy tells us very clearly that while there are some universals in terms of calming music (such as a slow, steady, heart-beat rhythm), personal choice is really the deciding factor. For example, we hear birds in a great deal of presumably calming music. No offense to our feathered friends, but the sounds of birds do not relax me, and in fact, they do the opposite. So, don't be surprised if your child doesn't like what you find relaxing.

Music also has the ability to change nervous system arousal, mood, and even affect motor systems (Tomaino, , 2019). Therefore, I recommend you guide your child in finding different kinds of music for the purpose of calming the body and/or uplifting mood. For books on music therapy and how to use music for self-regulation, please see the work of Dr. Dorita S. Berger.

Dr. Jennifer Jo Brout

Using Calming Activities Proactively (Anticipatory Anxiety)

Many people with misophonia experience anticipatory anxiety. That is, they become anxious when they know they may be faced with triggers. Although this is natural, anticipatory anxiety serves to elevate the sympathetic system. In other words, with anticipatory anxiety at work, your child is going from *50 to 90* rather than *0 to 60*. So, if you are planning a family outing in which you think your child may face triggers, use physiological calming exercises before you go. In sum, use these activities proactively, but also use them to help calm a dysregulated child if the situation allows.

The Tricky Translation

The trick in using these strategies is to translate them into the misophonic moment. In other words, being swaddled in a warm blanket may be calming to me even as an adult, yet if I were sitting in a classroom or giving a presentation it would be both untimely and a bit strange if I were to suddenly wrap myself in a weighted blanket. Certainly, I would not be able to jump into a warm bath! The following lists activities that help self-regulation based on the same principles but can be done in the moment. Again, these activities are not a cure-all, but each is a part of a toolbox that will ultimately give your child the ability to better manage misophonia. You will also find a copy of *Translational Activities (Worksheet #2)* at the end of the manual.

Translational Activities (Worksheet #2)
4 Square breathing
Chewable necklaces or bracelets
Fidget devices
Hand gripper
Hand massage using pressure points
Placing of palms together with pressure
Placing something heavy (coat or backpack) on lap
Soothing visual stimuli

Examples of Translational Activities

4 Square breathing. 4 square breathing is an exercise where individuals inhale their breath for the count of 4 seconds, then hold their breath for 4 seconds. Then, exhale for 4 seconds and then hold the breath for 4 seconds again. If 4 seconds is too difficult, a child can do this using 2 or 3 second intervals. Repeat until calm. In fact, there are numerous versions of this technique, all of which can be found on YouTube.

Fidget devices. Fidget devices are common tools used for people with various issues and can be found in toy stores. Some fidget device examples are fidget spinners and puzzle cubes. These devices, however, might not be a choice tool for families who have multiple misophonic children since fidgeting is a common visual/movement trigger. However, they are excellent for releasing tension.

Hand gripper. Often used in physical therapy or for guitar/bass players, hand grippers are squeezed and create tension or pressure. They offer intense proprioceptive input and work on the same principle as a stress ball. Stress balls, however, simply do not supply enough resistance for most with misophonia. In using hand grippers, make sure to supervise your child so that they don't incur an injury. Also, I advise purchasing the kind with variable tension.

Hand massage using pressure points. Massages to the hands are a common way to provide input to the pressure points that activate physiological calming. Hand massaging can be done anywhere, anytime, without others noticing. It is an excellent alternative to the hand gripper as it does not involve any equipment. Again, it is important to remember that for those with misophonia it takes more input into the muscles and joints to affect calm. Allow your child to adjust the pressure with which they feel the massage is most helpful.

Placing of palms together with pressure. In a similar manner, placing the palms together is an easy way to provide sensory input that is de-escalating to a child with misophonia. Your child can learn to do this with variable versions of pressure depending on personal preference.

Placing something heavy on lap. While any heavy object can be used, *weighted lap pads* are smaller and more readily available. However, as an alternative, a backpack or a heavy book can also be used to provide heavy pressure that provides calming input.

Soothing visual stimuli. Looking at something calming can also be very helpful. Examples of soothing visual stimuli that can be calming are paintings or artwork, fireplaces and crackling fires, aquariums, and running water such as streams and waterfalls.

Resetting the System

I want to emphasize that all of these sensory-based activities reset the nervous system. Resetting the nervous system is much easier to do in the absence of a trigger. When a child is triggered and asks others to stop making a particular noise, we know it is time for that child to reset his or her system. The purpose of resetting the system is so that a child can return to a situation with decreased sympathetic arousal using one of the proactive and/or in-the-moment activities.

You may find that your child at times does not want to leave the family room. The most likely reasons are because the child doesn't have strategies to calm down, is conflicted, or doesn't want to be alone. This is where co-regulation comes in Although it may not always be possible, in these instances, I suggest that it is best for a parent or caregiver to leave the room with your child and employ co-regulation.

Remember that co-regulation does not necessarily mean picking up your 9-year-old child and swaddling him or her. Instead, think of co-regulation as being your child's partner in their journey toward self-regulation. You can co-regulate by making suggestions in terms of what might help, reminding your child of strategies, and including yourself in an activity, which may at times be the best solution. A hug is also a form of co-regulation. Children will eventually learn to regulate on their own.

Summary

In this section, I have provided practical sensory-based and physiologically based strategies that I learned alongside my daughter when she was young. I realized at that time that for both of us, mind over matter alone was just not going to work, and I was lucky that I found some wonderful occupational therapists who individualized our sensory profiles and helped us each to understand how to better self-regulate. Yet, the problem we both still had was the in-the-moment reactivity. Since nobody knew how specific misophonia was, nobody understood that the down-regulating activities had to be translated into the moment of the misophonic response. That is why I call it the tricky translation. Regardless, both naturally relaxing activities and exercise as well as the in-the-moment activities are important, and it is essential to understand the difference. As we move on to the next section, I will address where the R for reasoning (use of cognitive skills) comes in. At the risk of repeating myself:

The reasoning skills are not any less important than the physiological, but they don't work until some physiological self-regulation is achieved.

5. Weaving the Three Rs Together

Putting together the three Rs is somewhat of an art that requires unpacking the multifaceted misophonic response into more manageable pieces for your child. We now know the rule of thumb is to regulate first when your child is highly escalated. In the previous section, we discussed in-depth sensory based methods that help self-regulation.

Now, however, we need to learn to shift amongst physiologically regulating activities and the other facets of coping skills. Remember, reasoning includes cognitive appraisal and reframing of thoughts, and reassurance means helping your child know that you are working together. This is not necessarily a linear process or a one-size-fits-all approach. Instead, weaving in between regulation, reasoning, and reassurance is somewhat like sculpting. Remember to refer to examples of corresponding worksheets and reminders in text here, and in full form later on. There is no precise order in which to use the worksheets. They are meant as tools for you to use as you chart your individualized course, on your own or with the assistance of a qualified therapist.

Understanding and Visualizing the Fight–Flight Response

As you already know, it is essential that you explain the idea of fight–flight to your child. Remember, it is the educative part of RRR that leads to the child's ability to understand what is happening to the body during misophonia reactivity. Depending on your individual child's age and capabilities, you may need to repeat or rephrase fight–flight several times as you and your child are working toward managing misophonia.

The *Fight–Flight (Reminder Sheet #2)* is useful to keep in your pocket. This is a quick reference guide that will help you explain fight–flight anytime you feel it would be helpful. If you are a parent, you know that when your child is dysregulated, it is often difficult for you to remain regulated and think clearly. The fight–flight reminder sheet will help you to focus your energy on something productive rather than falling into the dysregulation trap with your child. Make plenty of copies of this sheet so that you always have it on hand.

If possible, write your own version that reflects how you would speak to your individual child. Older children and adolescents can also write their own versions as well as illustrate them.

Fight–Flight

What Is the Fight–Flight Response?

The fight–flight response is a natural response in which the body prepares itself to deal with dangerous situations. When we are faced with a pressing danger, our bodies get us ready to fight the danger or escape from it.

What Does This Mean for Misophonia?

When dealing with misophonia, we find that the brain misinterprets trigger sounds as dangerous. The brain then sets off the fight–flight response to protect the individual from the perceived danger. This response signals the misophonia sufferer to experience this reaction and the symptoms that come with it such as sweating, rapid heartbeat, and hormonal changes. These are the most frequent symptoms, and they can happen at inappropriate times.

How Can I Explain Fight–Flight to My Child?

Depending on your child's age, you will need to modify your description of this process. For a very young child, you might focus on how fight–flight makes different parts of your child's body feel. With an older child or adolescent, you can start to explain how the brain sets off this process; it is meant to get us ready to fight danger, but can sometimes be set off by mistake. It may be helpful to employ examples of times fight–flight should be set off. For example, you may say to your child, "When you saw a bee in the backyard, and you ran inside, that was fight–flight working the right way."

Keeping Track of Triggers

Many children are aware of what their triggers are. However, I suggest using the *Keeping Track of Triggers*

(*Worksheet #3*) for several reasons. This simple worksheet helps parents to better understand what sounds/visuals trigger their child. Don't drive yourself crazy trying to keep precise data. This exercise is only meant to help you get an idea of the "what, when, and where" of triggers.

Observe your child at different times of the day and complete the boxes as best you can. If your child is old enough to list triggers, allow your child to do this independently, or you can do it together. Although we don't have the ability to anticipate all triggers, you might note that certain triggers happen in somewhat predictable places such as the kitchen or in the family room.

In addition, you may find that your child is more reactive at specific times of the day. For example, your child may be more reactive to triggers in the evening. By noting your child's trigger times and situations, you may find it helps ease your child's anxiety and helps you plan ahead and take proactive steps to lowering trigger exposure or utilize strategies at appropriate times.

Finally, using *Keeping Track of Triggers* (*Worksheet #3)* with your child, or comparing notes, is a good way to establish that you are going to be your child's partner in this process.

Keeping Track of Triggers (Worksheet #3)	
Sounds/visuals that bother child	When/where child experiences sound–visual

Separating the Physiological and the Emotional

As we unpack the misophonia response, we are almost constantly faced with helping the child separate the neurophysiological from the *emotion word*. Do your best to educate your child and emphasize the distinctions between reactivity and emotion, especially anger. Explain that the *sound* is making your child feel like running away, and if they cannot run away, then their body gets ready to fight. However, that feeling in the body is arguably not in and of itself an emotion.

Again, this process is an unnatural breaking down of a response that feels as though it is happening simultaneously. However, once a child understands the subtle similarities and differences between these interacting components, then there is room to work on them individually, thereby rendering a misophonic reaction much less daunting.

The *Misophonia Reaction (Worksheet #4)* is often a useful tool to help separate the physiological response from the idea of an emotion. This worksheet specifically helps to separate trigger sounds/visuals from feelings, thoughts, words, and actions. Again, using this worksheet and doing this exercise is not meant to be a stringent data mining process. The last thing a parent needs is more stress. Instead, use it as best you can as a source of information for both you and your child. This worksheet can be used repeatedly. Try to engage your child in doing this activity with you by explaining that it is like a game. If your child is very young or resistant to this, use the modified *Misophonic Reaction—Modified (Worksheet #5)* that is less weighty at the beginning and move toward using the more comprehensive worksheet *Misophonia Reaction (Worksheet #4)*

Misophonic Reaction (Worksheet #4)

Sound or Visual	Physical Reaction	Emotion Word	Thoughts	Actions

Misophonic Reaction—Modified (Worksheet #5)

Sound/visual trigger	Physiological response	Emotion word

Knowing How Much Time Your Child Needs to Calm

Monitoring regulation, or more specifically habituation, is another way to help your child both focus on the physiological and separate the physiological from the emotion words. Remember, habituation is the de-escalation of the sympathetic nervous system back to its neutral state and is what we are striving for.

In a sense, this is a little bit of biofeedback that one can experience at home without great expenditure of financial and other resources. Although these are very gross measures of the physiological system, one can use a heart monitor or a pulse monitor to track their child's baseline heart–pulse rate. In a lab, one would use something akin to a lie detector test called a *galvanic skin response.* The galvanic skin response test is a more direct measure of the sympathetic nervous system as it measures sweat gland activity. Regardless, it is fine to use these less complicated measures, and today, many people already have apps or devices that serve this purpose.

The *Monitoring Habituation (Worksheet #6)* is a way of recording how long it takes your child to habituate. However, the purpose of the exercise goes beyond just recording a measurement. From my experience doing this exercise with children and adolescents, I have found that they are surprised to find that their body goes back to neutral much more quickly than they thought. That is why I always ask both child and parent to first guess how long they each think it will take for habituation to occur.

Often, children will say that it takes them a half hour to an hour to calm down. Yet, in reality, it requires much less time. Research has not vetted a typical time that children reach habituation after misophonia reactivity. However, clinically, I have seen a range from 30 seconds to 10 minutes. Notably, there is likely a large variation in terms of how long it takes for children to habituate. In addition, the time it takes your individual child may depend on other contextual circumstances. Like the other exercises, remember this is not meant to be a great work of science, but rather it is something to help you and your child gain insight into misophonia and physiological functioning.

This is not an exercise that has to be repeated over and over again. Doing it even one time sends the message. As long as your child takes less time to habituate then originally stated, this is often the "aha!" moment. It is also encouraging for a parent to know that their child needs less time to de-escalate than one may have imagined. Everyone feels more in control.

There is also a more advanced version of this exercise that I often use with older children and adolescents. Adolescents can often do these exercises independently. The more advanced exercise includes the original set of steps but adding one of the sensory-based techniques to see if that helps habituation happen more quickly. This is the exercise that often gets older children to buy into these coping-skills methods, thereby encouraging them to do the work.

Monitoring Habituation Instructions (Reminder Sheet #5)

Step 1: Take a guess at how long you think it takes your child to calm down after being triggered.

Step 2: Ask your child the same question. Most parents, children, and adolescents guess that the process is much longer than it actually is. Once an individual is away from the offending *stimulus*, the de-escalating usually happens very quickly (in as little as 30 seconds).

Step 3: Take a baseline measurement of heart–pulse rate three times a day when your child is calm (in neutral) and average that.

Step 4: When triggered, remove your child away from the offending stimulus and follow the rate of de-escalation.

- Measure heart–pulse after your child is triggered (although this is not what we are looking for).
- Continue to measure until your child is at baseline.
- Record the time it took for your child to reach baseline.

Monitoring Habituation Recording Information (Worksheet #6)		
Time of trigger	Time back to baseline	Difference (time of habituation)
6:03	6:30	30 sec.

What If This Doesn't Work?

If you find that your child is not habituating after being removed from the offending stimulus, then we know that there are other issues at play. For example, some children will continue to ruminate over the trigger sound or about the person from whom the sound emanated. In this case, we can point this out to a child or have the child do exercises to quickly end rumination. The best way to end rumination involves getting out of the mind and into the body, which can be a sensory-based exercise that requires more strenuous movement or may be accomplished by listening to music.

Movement in General (Releasing Adrenaline)

You may have noticed that many, although not all, of the sensory strategies involve movement. Movement is such a powerful tool in terms of de-escalating the sympathetic system that it warrants some extra attention. To see how powerful movement is, simply note the difference of how much reactivity your child experiences when he or she is truly moving such as running, skateboarding, dancing, or otherwise.

I have asked many children and adolescents this question: "Do you have any misophonia reactivity when you are in a pool, running, or skateboarding?" Almost all have answered, "No." Often, this is a welcomed revelation as children and adolescents realize that there are times in the day when reactivity is significantly decreased or even absent.

Finally, movement also demands attention. Remember preattention in which the brain focuses on what is salient in the environment? Our preattention must go to our body's movement when we are navigating space. Our brains still scan for stimuli in the environment to warn us of danger, but our preattention is more focused on the activity and not on external sound and visual stimuli.

One technique I have found helpful is the *adrenaline release*. We have reviewed proactive calming techniques and sensory-based methods to bring down nervous system reactivity. However, what do we do when our child is in full "meltdown mode" or nearing it?

As we have learned, if you can remove your child from the offending stimulus, then do so until homeostasis is reached. *Regulate first*. However, there are ways to help your child learn how to release the adrenaline associated with fight–flight. We have talked about bringing in the parasympathetic system which brakes fight–flight. Some children also need to release the adrenaline that circulates when the system is triggered. The *Adrenaline Release (Reminder Sheet #3)* provides positive ways for a child to do this. You will see that some of the suggestions overlap with sensory-based techniques.

Adrenaline Release (Reminder Sheet #3)

Step 1: Review the activity with your child; explain the purpose to enlist your child's cooperation.

Step 2: Brainstorm with your child about which activities will serve the purpose of adrenaline release. If use of the word "adrenaline" is too elusive to your child, you can say, "to get out the bad energy," or whatever you think will communicate the concept best.

Step 3: Brainstorm a cue word that you will say to your child when you see escalation occurring.

The goal of this exercise is to release the adrenaline but also to change negative valence to positive valence. Remember, valence is a qualifier to the sympathetic nervous system arousal level. The idea is to put in to place an activity that a child can do in the moment at home, though not necessarily something a child would do at school or in public. These activities may be modified to be used at school and even in public.

When a child seems as though an explosion or meltdown is inevitable, guide them to do heavy physical activity. Before doing this in real time, however, brainstorm with your child as to what activities might work. Examples are doing push-ups, jumping up and down, running in place, jumping jacks, and so forth. Because you and your child have already discussed these activities, simply remind your child to start doing jumping jacks. Children often find it fun to have a code word that might remind them to do their activity like "activate."

Many of these activities can work easily in the home since it is often possible to stop what one is doing and proceed with this exercise. I have known children and adolescents who have permission to leave the classroom, quickly do these exercises in the hallway or in a place designated by the school, and this has been very helpful to stave off misophonic meltdowns. This also means classmates are not staring at your child. In addition, something like the hand-gripper, which requires more output, may help your child outside of the house.

Summary

The most important idea to remember in terms of weaving together RRR is that it is not a one-size-fits-all prescription. This is why I feel it is often best for parents to take the wheel, even if they feel they need a therapist's guidance. Ultimately, parents know their child best. Parents know their child's preferences, their natural rhythms, and ultimately how to individualize coping skills so that they work best for their unique situation. A therapist for misophonia is best when she hands the keys to the parents and to the child—the keys to self-regulation. Again, adolescents are often able to work more independently or with the guidance of a therapist.

In the next section, I address the typical issues that arise regarding family functioning in misophonia. Anyone who has a child or adolescent with misophonia knows that the family system is affected. Yet, this too can be remediated.

6. Family Dynamics

The dynamics related to misophonia are highly complex and would be best covered in a dedicated workbook. However, for now, it helps to go over the basics. As we do this, more worksheets are included to assist you.

A child with misophonia often feels victimized by the overwhelming auditory/visual stimuli that other family members generate. However, siblings also may feel victimized by the misophonic child's sudden unpredictable words or actions. In general, it helps to let siblings know:

- Their feelings are valid, and you are concerned about them as well.
- You appreciate any help they give you in terms of their sibling.
- You are working on coping skills, and everything is going

to get better (weaving in reassurance).

It also helps to explain misophonia to siblings and emphasize that when they generate sounds that bother their sibling, it is not their fault.

As we move toward better physiological regulation and cognitive reframing, we will begin to work on how your child perceives or thinks about trigger sounds. In misophonia, individuals often associate the sounds and visuals that trigger them with specific people. I often hear statements such as, "My sister is my worst trigger," or, "My father triggers me the worst." Unfortunately, science has not established why the sounds and visuals of some people may be worse than those of others. While it is true that there seems to be an orientation around person-based types of sounds, trigger sound and visuals are not exclusive to mouth sounds and are certainly not exclusive to *people sounds*. Sounds such as windshield wipers, the sound of rain, pen clicking, beeping from electronic devices, and pets are among the various nonhuman sources that individuals with misophonia frequently describe as triggering (Brout et al., 2015; Jastreboff & Jastreboff, 2001).

Thus, focusing on people rather than the sound/visual as the source only makes things worse. Focusing on the person brings in a dynamic between the misophonic individual and another that simply makes both the condition and relationship worse. Therefore, it is highly imperative to change this narrative in terms of how the individual with misophonia thinks regarding the whole family. Next, I address cognitive strategies that are pertinent to the individual and also relate to the family system. In addition, this section addresses practical family-based strategies that can help assuage misophonia related family stress.

Separating Triggers from People

One of the easiest ways to help your child separate trigger sounds and visuals from people is through _psychoeducation_. You can certainly try explaining to your child that a particular noise—that is, their sibling's whistling, not their sibling—upsets them. Adolescents often understand this, but it may be helpful to utilize reading material written by a professional or by others with misophonia rather than your own explanation. Sometimes, and most especially for younger children, explanation is not enough. This is something only you as a parent can assess. For younger children, it is often helpful to go beyond verbally based psychoeducation by supplying a concrete example to children.

Separating Triggers from People (younger children) (Worksheet # 7) will guide you through this exercise. The concept behind this activity is to create a concrete symbol for trigger sounds/visuals. By concrete, I mean something your child can hold in the hands. Your child, like so many, has associated the trigger with a specific person, and we must try to undo that association. Although it may be difficult to disassociate memories that have paired together, we can begin with this exercise.

Preparation: Before you begin, pick one or two specific situations or places related to corresponding triggers. For example, choose the kitchen and eating or the family room and sniffling, etc. If your child positively reacts, you can do this more than once a day. For example, you might try it at two meals or three; however, don't try to do more than that.

Step 1: Have your child draw a picture of a mouth and call it *Mr. Chewy* or *Ms. Breathing*. Card stock is preferable since it is more durable, but paper will do just fine. You can also use play dough or other types of clay to make these figurines. I also like to use *emoticon balls* which are stress balls that have different emotions printed on them.

Step 2: After your child has drawn and characterized triggers or you have purchased the emoticon balls, challenge your child to refrain from referring to family members as their trigger, and it is important for everyone in the family to do the same. Here, each drawing or figurine has a sound and correlating name. If you are using the emoticon balls, have your child label them Mr. Chewy, Ms. Sneezy, etc.

Step 3: Then, when you are at dinner, for example, and your child says something akin to, "You are triggering me," to someone who is chewing, have the child turn around so that they are not facing the person from whom the trigger is emanating.

Step 4: Hand them their drawing or emoticon balls (*Mr. Chewy*), and encourage them to talk to the sound or visual such as, "I can't stand you, *Mr. Chewy*." It is essential that you treat this like a game and an exercise, never as something punitive.

Young children will usually enjoy this, and older children may think this is silly or embarrassing. However, encourage your child to try it just once. It is not the exercise itself that engenders change as much as it solidifies the point we are trying to make. It helps change the narrative.

Of course, your child will not use emoticon balls or pictures forever, and some children grow bored with this exercise quickly. However, as your child learns self-regulation skills and the narrative changes, we see behaviors such as making faces at others, mimicking others, and verbal aggressions fade away.

Some Reassurance from Me to You

For those children who do tend to react toward others, all of these exercises will help them understand that there are more constructive ways to release the negative energy that builds up from misophonia. This may take more time for some children than others, but gentle reminders along the way reinforce the groundwork. With the foundation there, parents can move toward making rules about how their misophonic child reacts to others. However, don't make the rules before you give your child the skills.

What if My Child Is Aggressive Toward Others or Self?

Unfortunately, many children with misophonia use their hands instead of their words, especially when they are very young. We now know that this is because the child is

87

overwhelmed by auditory/visual stimuli, is in fight–flight mode, and cognition is not readily accessible. For children who tend to be more physical, it often takes more strenuous work for sensory–physiological changes to take place. Before continuing, I do want to make clear that every family should have a policy in which nobody is allowed to physically hurt others, even a child with misophonia. I want to discuss ways that you can divert aggression so that you have some practical skills to help your child.

Family Negotiations

As we know, problems often occur when siblings and/or when the whole family is together. In the beginning, while your child is still developing coping skills, it is best to encourage your child to leave the room. Fleeing the stimulus is, in fact, adaptive. It is the *flight* part of fight–flight. It is what the brain tells us to do. It also gives the message to the misophonic child that he or she needs to act in terms of helping him or herself rather than always depending on others for accommodation. In the section, "More About Family Accommodations and Preserving Sibling Relationships," I will go over ideas regarding how much to accommodate your child and when and how to enlist the help of sibling(s).

Developing Perspective Taking, Family Rules, Empathy for Family Members

Here is an exercise that I always like to use for children, adolescents, and adults who help the individual think through the nature of their triggers, particularly ones that are person-centered. Every now and then, I hear about a sibling using trigger sounds against their misophonic brother or sister. Certainly, this should not be allowed. However, sometimes, it might seem like noises exist only to bother the misophonic individual. If a child is tired, sick, or in a bad mood and hears someone making one of their trigger sounds, the child might feel like they are doing it on purpose.

Although there are some noises that people make on purpose, many are noises that people must make and that they cannot help. These are noises that people make unintentionally for their health. It can be helpful to figure out which noises people *need to make*, and which noises they *do not* need to make.

Of course, this exercise should be done when your child is calm. It can be an efficient way to help your child understand that people from whom triggers emanate are not doing so on purpose. This exercise will also help your child develop perspective-taking skills and even empathy for others in the context of misophonia.

You will find the worksheet *Necessary, Unnecessary, & Habitual Sounds (Worksheet # 8)* in Section 8. Here, a child simply categorizes sounds and visuals into those that are necessary to sustain life, those that are not, and those that are habitual in nature. While I am using the most obvious words to express these concepts here, please feel free to use your own words that reflect the culture of your family.

As you go through this process with your child, it becomes painfully obvious that most trigger sounds fall within the *necessary* category. Breathing and eating are the best examples of this. Other sounds/visuals are necessary and spontaneous because they either serve a physical comfort or health purpose. Examples of these are sneezing and throat clearing. Sneezing is spontaneous and throat clearing is necessary to free obstructions. Of course, this isn't a perfect science, and some of these triggers, like throat clearing, can also be habitual.

In terms of habitual sounds/visuals, a parent may even explain to their child, "Your brother shakes his leg because he is nervous," or, "He needs some way of releasing his stress just like you." Again, this explanation engenders empathy. The use of empathy is very important in misophonia because it is easy to fall into the trappings of blame where one feels like people are attacking them, when in essence, sensory stimuli is.

You can use this list to make family negotiations. For example, when a person produces necessary sounds/visuals, it is up to the individual to leave the room and do a nervous system reset or use other strategies. If someone in the family, for example, is tapping on their phone, you might consider this unnecessary and ask them to leave the room or simply turn off the sound. Don't expect these rules to work perfectly. The important idea here is that you are helping your child to change the narrative.

Necessary, Unnecessary, & Habitual Sounds (Worksheet #8)		
Necessary sounds/visuals	Unnecessary sounds/visuals	Habit sounds/visuals

More About Family Accommodations and Preserving Sibling Relationships

While it may be painful for parents to do so, I think it is important that you are realistic when explaining to your misophonic child the extent to which the world will and will not be accommodating. You want your child to understand that you and other family members are willing to make accommodations to ease the burden of misophonia. However, this is not always possible, especially in the outside world.

Also, it is important for the child with misophonia to understand that their reactivity, if it is focused on another person, it is hurtful. Siblings also must learn as much as possible about the disorder so that they understand why your child with misophonia is doing what they are doing. As a parent, you walk a fine line between emphasizing the physiological underpinnings of misophonia and deemphasizing the emotional component while recognizing your child and siblings' feelings.

If your child lashes out at a sibling, your child must apologize once regulated, and their sibling should be encouraged to understand and accept the apology. This helps to preserve the relationship.

Certainly, parents should try to model this behavior. However, it is also helpful to do a *redo*. This gives everyone in the family a chance to modify their behavior in a calm environment. *"The Redo" (Reminder Sheet #4)* serves as a reminder of this strategy.

Because we know from the family systems theory that when one person in the family is dysregulated, other family members tend to also become dysregulated, we can call this *group dysregulation*. We also know from family systems that if one person in the family makes a change, the system itself changes.

93

Therefore, if one person in the family makes a positive shift within the dysregulated dynamic, the whole family will benefit. If your family has just experienced group dysregulation, without placing blame on anyone, suggest that your family does a redo.

Simply ask family members to think about what happened and what they might do differently to make the situation better. Ask people to speak aloud about their ideas. You can certainly help your misophonic child as well as siblings to develop their ideas. This is especially important if you have very young children. When everybody has a clear idea of what they are going to try, proceed to actually do a redo of what occurred. Do not recreate the trigger sound/visual for your child. Instead, use a neutral sound for the redo.

You may find certain family members are uncooperative or may not want to participate at that time. Yet, this is still an excellent exercise even if it doesn't involve the whole family or all the family members who were part of the dysregulated group. Remember, in the family systems theory, if one person in the family makes a positive change, the whole system alters for the better.

Summary

Family life is almost always negatively impacted by misophonia. This is made even more stressful as so many family therapists don't yet know about misophonia and are therefore unable to jump in and help. However, the ideas listed above will help you to avoid or begin to mend family problems. If you feel as though your family needs more help than this workbook provides, please reach out to one of the centers or institutions studying misophonia and ask them to help you find a family therapist. Alternatively, you may have your own family therapist reach out to a misophonia specialist. Knowledge of misophonia is gaining ground quickly, and a variety of practitioners will have the opportunity to learn how to support those with misophonia and their families.

7. Conclusion

With misophonia, there are always going to be ups and downs. You should expect variability in what you see at home, at school, and during social activities. Most parents don't automatically understand, and often, teachers ask the same question: "Why is so-and-so great during one class and not during another?" or, "Why can they eat with one friend and not another?" These types of assumptions often, unfortunately, turn into parent or victim blaming. As stated earlier, people may tell you that your child is manipulating you or using this condition to run the household, the school classroom, or that you are too indulgent. However, remember variability in misophonia is absolutely typical.

Research has not yet vetted this out, but most agree that these are some mediating factors in misophonia:

- Poor sleep
- General health
- Mood
- Anxiety and stress

As your child ages, you will likely want to promote your child's ability to take charge of their misophonia management. Given this reality, it is beneficial to teach your child to advocate for him or herself. There may be times your child can use self-regulatory techniques to handle certain situations. There may be times that your child may ask somebody to modify their behavior. There may be times when your child has to leave the room. Learning how and when to use each strategy involves you and your child's engagement in self-monitoring and expectation management.

Do keep in mind a note of reassurance for yourself: the process gets easier as it goes along and as children grow. The goal here is to move from co-regulation to self-regulation, just as it is in typical child rearing. However, you are doing so with a child who faces specific difficulty in their ability to self-regulate. Therefore, self-regulation for your child may come slowly, but it *will* progress. Your misophonic child needs a great deal of reassurance throughout their development. Your child will have to overcome specific challenges, but that does not have to stop them from living a happy life.

8. Worksheets and Reminder Sheets

This section is available as a Word document on our website. The Word format allows you to edit the sheets with your own words.

Please go to www.misophoniaeducation.com/worksheets and enter the password "manualsheets" to download your copies for free as part of ownership of this manual. These worksheets are formatted for standard letter-sized paper.

Reminder Sheets

Be Sensible (Reminder Sheet #1)

- **Sight** (Vision)
- **Hearing** (Auditory)
- **Smell** (Olfactory)
- **Taste** (Gustatory)
- **Touch** (Tactile)
- **Interoception** (what we feel inside our bodies)
- **Vestibular** (sense of balance and rotation)
- **Proprioception** (sense of where our bodies our in space)

Fight–Flight (Reminder Sheet #2)

What is the fight–flight response?

- The body's way of preparing itself to deal with dangerous situations when we are faced with a pressing danger; our bodies get us ready to fight the danger or escape it.

What does this mean for misophonia?

- When one is dealing with misophonia, the brain misinterprets trigger sounds as dangerous.
- The brain then sets off the fight–flight response to protect the individual from the perceived danger.
- This means that a misophonia sufferer will experience this reaction and the symptoms that come with it such as sweating, rapid heartbeat, and hormonal changes more frequently than others.

How can I explain fight–flight to my child?

- For a very young child, you might focus on how fight–flight makes different parts of your child's body feel.
- With an older child or adolescent, you can start to

explain how the brain sets off this process which is meant to get us ready to fight danger but can sometimes be set off by mistake.

- It may be helpful to employ examples of times fight–flight should be set off (i.e. "When you saw a bee in the backyard and you ran inside, that was fight–flight working the right way.").

Make your own reference sheet in your own words and based on how best to explain and remind your child what fight–flight is.

Adrenaline Release (Reminder Sheet #3)

Step 1: Review the activity with your child; explain the purpose in order to enlist your child's cooperation.

Step 2: Brainstorm with your child about which activities will serve the purpose of adrenaline release.

- If use of the word "adrenaline" is too elusive to your child, you can say, "to get out the bad energy," or whatever you think will communicate the concept best.

Step 3: Brainstorm a cue word that you will say to your child when you see escalation occurring.

The Redo (Reminder Sheet #4)

- Remember, when your child becomes dysregulated, the whole family may become dysregulated.
- We can call this group dysregulation.
- We also know from family systems that if one person in the family makes a change, the system itself changes.
- Therefore, if one person in the family makes a positive shift within the dysregulated dynamic, the whole family will benefit.
- If your family has just experienced group dysregulation, without placing blame on anyone in particular, suggest that your family does a redo.
- Simply ask family members to think about what happened and what they might do differently to make the situation better.
- Ask people to speak aloud about their ideas. You can certainly help your misophonic child as well as siblings to develop their ideas.
- This is especially important if you have very young children.
- When everybody has a clear idea of what they are going

to try, proceed to actually do a redo of what occurred.

- Do not recreate the trigger sound/visual for your child. Instead, use a neutral sound for the redo.

- You may find certain family members are uncooperative or do not want to participate. Yet, this is still an excellent exercise even if it doesn't involve the whole family or all of the family members who were part of the dysregulated group.

Monitoring Habituation Instructions (Reminder Sheet #5)

Step 1: Take a guess at how long you think it takes your child to calm down after being triggered.

Step 2: Ask your child the same question. Most parents, children, and adolescents guess that the process is much longer than it actually is. *Once an individual is away from the offending stimulus, the de-escalating usually happens very quickly (in as little as 30 seconds).*

Step 3: Take a baseline measurement of heart/pulse rate three times a day when your child is calm (in neutral) and average that.

Step 4: When triggered, remove your child away from the offending stimulus and follow the rate of de-escalation.

- Measure heart–pulse after your child is triggered (*although this is not what we are looking for*).
- Continue to measure until your child is at baseline.
- Record the time it took for your child to reach baseline

Keeping Arousal Low at Home: Relaxing Activities–Everyday Practice (Worksheet #1)

Massage (foot rollers, hand rollers, etc.)
Rocking (or gliding) in chair
Rocking (or gliding) in chair with weighted blanket
Rolling on the floor or mat
Stretching
Taking a bath
Weighted blanket
Yoga
Write your own activities here.

Translational Activities (Worksheet #2)
4 Square breathing
Chewable necklaces or bracelets
Fidget devices
Hand gripper
Hand massage using pressure points
Placing of palms together with pressure
Placing something heavy (coat or backpack) on lap
Soothing visual stimuli
Write in your child's favorites here and add any ideas you have.

Keeping Track of Triggers (Worksheet #3)

Sounds/visuals that bother child	When/where child experiences sound/visual

Misophonic Reaction (Worksheet #4)

Sound/visual	Physical reaction	Emotion word	Thoughts	Actions

Misophonic Reaction—Modified (Worksheet #5)

Sound/visual trigger	Physiological response	Emotion word

Dr. Jennifer Jo Brout

Monitoring Habituation (Worksheet #6)

Time of trigger	Time back to baseline	Difference (time of habituation)
6:03	6:30	30 sec.

Separating Triggers from People (Worksheet #7)

- Before you begin, pick one or two specific situations–places related to corresponding triggers. For example, choose the kitchen and eating or the family room and sniffling, etc. If your child reacts positively, you can do this more than once a day. For example, you might try it at two meals or three. However, don't try to do more than that.

- Have your child draw a picture of a mouth and call it *Mr. Chewy* or *Ms. Breathing*. Card stock is preferable since it is more durable, but paper will do just fine. You can also use play dough or other types of clay to make these figurines.

- I also like to use emoticon balls which are stress balls that have different emotions printed on them.

- After your child has drawn and characterized triggers or you have purchased the emoticon balls, challenge your child to refrain from referring to family members as their trigger, and it is important for everyone in the family to do the same.

- If you are using the emoticon balls, have your child label them *Mr. Chewy, Ms. Sneezy*, etc.

- Then, when you are at dinner, for example, and your child says something akin to, "You are triggering me," to someone who is chewing, have the child turn around so that they are not facing the person from whom the trigger is emanating.
- Hand them their drawing or emoticon balls (*Mr. Chewy*) and encourage them to talk to the sound or visual, saying something like, "**I can't stand you,** *Mr. Chewy*." It is essential that you treat this like a game and an exercise, never as something punitive.
- Young children will usually enjoy this, and older children may think this is silly or embarrassing. However, encourage your child to try it just once. It is not the exercise itself that engenders change as much as it solidifies the point we are trying to make. It helps change the narrative.

Necessary, Unnecessary, & Habitual Sounds (Worksheet #8)

Necessary sounds/visuals	Unnecessary sounds/visuals	Habitual sounds/visuals

Dr. Jennifer Jo Brout

RRR Classes

Find classes at www.misophoniaeducation.com/regulate-reason-reassure/

This class provides an accessible way to learn the basics of coping with misophonia and is a comprehensive coping skills approach designed for parents to use with their children and teens.

This is a 2-week class featuring 4 classes that are 2 hours each. All classes will be recorded and have a 30-minute question period included. These classes will be recorded and you can join during the meeting, or watch the videos after. You can also alternate watching videos and being there live.

"I built this class because so many people were contacting me and wanting to know my approach for coping skills and I was thinking of a way to make it more affordable for parents than recurring counselling sessions because parents helping their children have so much power to help their child cope, especially since there are so few providers for misophonia coping skills."

— Dr. Jennifer Jo Brout

Dr. Jennifer Jo Brout

Glossary

Acceptance and commitment therapy (ACT)

A type of therapy based on feeling one's emotions (not avoiding them), changing the way one interacts or relates to their thoughts, and being present without judgment (Hayes et al, 2006).

Amygdala

A part of the brain that is activated automatically by external threat and bodily fear responses (e.g., changes in perspiration, heart rate, pupil size; LeDoux, 2012).

Anxiety

Persistent worries and fears that are absent of an external stressor often leading to insomnia, irritability, anger, fatigue, and muscle tension (Alvord & Halfond, 2019).

Arousal

The physiological state of "alertness" in the human body. High arousal could be indicated by rapid heartbeat and muscle tension, whereas slow heart rate and long slow breathing indicate low arousal (Brown & Bowman, 2002).

Auditory sensory gating

The process by which the brain adjusts to stimuli. This is the brain's way of taking in important auditory information while diverting attention from unnecessary sounds (Cromwell et al., 2008)

Autism spectrum disorder (ASD)

A disorder where one has difficulty communicating and interacting with others, restricts interests, and has repetitive behaviors (The National Institute of Mental Health, 2018).

Autonomic nervous system (ANS)

A major part of the peripheral (non-brain or spinal cord) nervous system. The ANS controls many unconscious processes in the body including the fight–flight reaction (Low, 2020).

Bottom-up processing

Using physical activities to help integrate the senses and impact nervous system arousal (Low, 2020).

Cognitive behavioral therapy (CBT)

A type of therapy based on changing thinking and behavioral patterns. CBT emphasizes an individual being their own therapist, focusing on present circumstances, and how to cope and move forward (American Psychological Association, 2017a).

Co-regulation

When a parent or caregiver assists an infant to calm after they experience a fight–flight response (American Psychological Association, n.d.).

Dialectical Behavior Therapy (DBT)

Dialectical behavior therapy (DBT) is a well-established treatment for borderline personality disorder (BPD) and has also been utilized as a therapy for emotional dysregulation regarding other disorders in which affect regulation is problematic. (Lynch, et. al, 2006).

Dysregulation

A state in which an individual's physical response is out of sync with his or her situation. For example, a person in a state of high arousal while lying quietly in bed (American Psychological Association, n.d.).

Ear, nose, and throat (ENT) specialist–otologist

A doctor specializing in the ears and hearing disorders.

Ego-dystonic

Behaviors that are not consistent with a person's view of him or herself. For example, a person who considers himself calm becoming angry and screaming at his family (American Psychological Association, n.d.).

Ego-syntonic

Behaviors that are consistent with a person's view of him or herself. For example, a person who considers himself calm remaining relaxed in an unpleasant situation (American Psychological Association, n.d.).

Electroencephalogram

A device used to measure electrical activity in the brain (Blocka, 2018).

Enteric nervous system

The enteric nervous system exerts a profound influence on all digestive processes, namely motility, ion transport, and gastrointestinal blood flow. Some of this control emanates from connections between the digestive system and central nervous system (Bowen, n.d.). For further information see http://www.vivo.colostate.edu/hbooks/pathphys/digestion/basics/gi_nervous.html

Epigenetics

The study of the process by which certain genes can be "turned on" within individuals. This is to say, a gene may be present in a person's genome but will become active or dormant depending external situations (Center for Disease Control, 2020).

Exposure therapy

A type of therapy that immerses one in their fears to reduce anxiety and decrease avoidance (American Psychological Association, 2017b).

Fight–flight (freeze-fight–flight)

An involuntary physical response that prepares the body to deal with a threatening situation in one of these three ways. The nervous system becomes aroused, quickening heart rate and tensing muscles. For purposes of describing misophonia, we concentrate on fight–flight (American Psychological Association, n.d.).

Gene

A discrete piece of a chromosome which determines heredity (American Psychological Association, n.d.).

Habituation

The process by which an individual becomes accustomed to a continuing stimulus and thus no longer alerts to it (Rankin et al, 2009).

Hyperacusis

An unusually high sensitivity to tolerate usual environmental sounds that results in exaggerated and/or inappropriate responses to those sounds (Baguley, 2003).

Hyperacusis retraining therapy

Retraining therapy that strives to reduce the patient's decreased tolerance to sound and have them view sound in a more positive manner. Sound generators, which resemble a small hearing aid, are often used to produce sounds that will help the patient habituate. Theoretically, by listening to sounds at a low level for a prescribed amount each day, the auditory nerves and brain will become desensitized. The treatment is often successful and takes between three months to two years (University of San Francisco, n.d.).

Mirror Neurons

Mirror neurons are a class of neuron that modulate their activity both when an individual executes a specific motor act and when they observe the same or similar act performed by another individual.

Misokinesia

A phenomenon in which individuals experience aversive responses to repetitive visual stimuli or movement. More research is required on misokinesia (Schröder et al., 2013).

Misophonia

A disorder in which sufferers experience strong, unpleasant reactions to certain, seemingly innocuous, sounds (Jastreboff & Jastreboff, 2001).

Neocortex

The most recently evolved part of the cerebral cortex in the brain that has six layers for primary sensory and motor cortex function (American Psychological Association, n.d.)

Obsessive-compulsive disorder (OCD)

A disorder characterized by recurrent, repetitive, intrusive, and unwanted thoughts and/or behaviors that someone feels obligated to perform to prevent anxiety (Phillips and Stein, 2018).

Obsessive-compulsive personality disorder (OCPD)

A disorder characterized by the persistent need to maintain things in an orderly manner, so much that it interferes with one's life (Merck Manual Editorial Staff, 2020).

Parasympathetic nervous system

The part of the ANS that returns the body to homeostasis when a threat is no longer present after experiencing a fight–flight reaction (American Psychological Association, n.d.).

Phonophobia

An unusually strong reaction of the autonomic system and limbic system resulting in fear of sounds (Jastreboff & Jastreboff, 2000).

Preattention

An unconscious process where the brain scans the environment using the body's senses (American Psychological Association, n.d.).

Stimulus

An external occurrence that evokes a reaction in an individual (American Psychological Association, n.d.).

Sympathetic nervous system

The part of the ANS that activates the flight-flight response when the body senses a threat (American Psychological Association, n.d.).

Self-regulation

The ability to use one's cognitive, physiological, and emotional resources to calm after the body experiences a fight–flight response.

Sensory processing disorder (SPD)

A disorder in which sufferers over or under-respond to some types of sensory stimuli. There are numerous subtypes. For example, Sensory Over Responsivity refers to individuals who respond more intensely to sensory stimuli than is typical. This can occur in one or more sensory modalities. For more information about SPD and its subtypes, see The Star Institute.

Tinnitus

A disorder characterized by an uncontrollable ringing in the ears with no discernable cause.

Tinnitus retraining therapy (TRT)

Tinnitus retraining therapy is often based on sound therapy as well as counseling. Sound therapy may include one or a combination of approaches including masking, distraction, and habituation, for example. Masking involves exposing the patient to an external noise at a loud enough volume that it partially or completely covers the tinnitus sound. Distraction uses an external sound to distract a patient from the tinnitus sound. Habituation involves helping the patient "reclassify tinnitus as an unimportant sound that should be ignored" (Jastreboff & Jastreboff, 2000).

Top-down processing

Using cognitive skills to replace negative thoughts with positive ones in order to affect the physiological state.

Valence

The positive or negative feeling that goes along with physical arousal (American Psychological Association, n.d.).

References

Alvord, M. A., & Halfond, R. (2019). *What's the Difference Between Stress and Anxiety?* American Psychological Association. https://www.apa.org/topics/stress-anxiety-difference.

American Psychological Association. (n.d.). *APA dictionary of psychology.* Retrieved March 5th, 2021, from https://dictionary.apa.org/

American Psychological Association. (2017). *What is cognitive behavioral therapy?* Div. 12 (Society of Clinical Psychology). https://www.apa.org/ptsd-guideline/patients-and-families/cognitive-behavioral#

American Psychological Association. (2017). *What is exposure therapy?* Div. 12 (Society of Clinical Psychology). https://www.apa.org/ptsd-guideline/patients-and-families/exposure-therapy

Baguley, D. M. (2003). Hyperacusis. *Journal of the Royal Society of Medicine, 96.* https://doi.org/10.1177%2F014107680309601203

Baguley, D. M., Cope, T. E., & McFerran, D. J. (2016). Functional auditory disorders. *Handbook of Clinical Neurology, 139,* 367–378. https://doi.org/10.1016/ B978-0-12-801772-2.00032-1

Bernstein, R., Angell, K., & Dehle, C. (2013). A brief course of cognitive behavioural therapy for the treatment of misophonia: A case example. *The Cognitive Behaviour*

Therapist, 6, E10.
https://doi.org/10.1017/S1754470X13000172

Bowlby, J. (1958). The nature of the child's tie to his mother. *International Journal of Psychoanalysis, 39,* 350–373.

The Bowen Center for the study of the family. (n.d.).
https://www.thebowencenter.org/

Brout, J. J., Edelstein, M., Erfanian, M., Mannino, M., Miller, L. J., Rouw, R., Kumar, S., & Rosenthal, M. Z. (2018). Investigating misophonia: A review of the empirical literature, clinical implications, and a research agenda. *Frontiers in Neuroscience, 12,*
https://doi.org/10.3389/fnins.2018.00036

Blocka, C. (2018) *What is an EEG?* Healthline.
https://www.healthline.com/health/eeg#:~:text=An%20el ectroencephalogram%20(EEG)%20is%20a,problems%20 associated%20with%20this%20activity

Brown, V. J., & Bowman, E. M., (2002). *Encyclopedia of the Human Brain.* Academic Press, 99–110,
https://doi.org/10.1016/B0-12-227210-2/00015-7

Cavanna, A. E., & Seri, S. (2015). Misophonia: current perspectives. *Neuropsychiatric Disease and Treatment, 11,* 2117–2123. https://doi.org/10.2147/NDT.S81438

Center for Disease Control, (2020). *What is epigenetics?* Genomics & Precision Health.
https://www.cdc.gov/genomics/disease/epigenetics.htm

Cromwell, H. C., Mears, R. P., Wan, L., & Boutros, N. N. (2008). Sensory gating: A translational effort from basic to clinical science. *Clinical EEG and Neuroscience,*

39(2), 69–72.
https://doi.org/10.1177/155005940803900209

Ferreira, G. M., Harrison, B. J., & Fontenelle, L. F. (2013). Hatred of sounds: Misophonic disorder or just an underreported psychiatric symptom? *Annals of Clinical Psychiatry, 25,* 271–274.

Gavin, W. J., Dotseth, A., Roush, K. K., Smith, C. A., Spain, H. D., & Davies, P. L. (2011). Electroencephalography in children with and without sensory processing disorders during auditory perception. *American Journal of Occupational Therapy, 65,* 370–377. https://doi.org/10.5014/ajot.2011.002055

Hayes, S. C., Luoma, J. B., Bond, F. W., Masuda, A., & Lillis, J. (2006). Acceptance and commitment therapy: Model, processes and outcomes. *Psychology Faculty Publications, 101.* https://scholarworks.gsu.edu/psych_facpub/101

Jastreboff, M. M., & Jastreboff, P. J. (2000). Tinnitus retraining therapy (TRT) as a method for treatment of tinnitus and hyperacusis patients. *Journal of American Audiology,* Issue 11, 162–177. http://neuroagility.com/wp-content/uploads/Jastreboff2000-Tinnitus_retraining_therapy_TRT_as_a_method_for_trea tment_and_hyperacusis_patients.pdf

Jastreboff, M. M., & Jastreboff, P. J. (2001). *Hyperacusis.* AudiologyOnline. June 18, 2001. https://www.audiologyonline.com/articles/hyperacusis-1223

Jastreboff, M. M., & Jastreboff, P. J. (2001). Components of decreased sound tolerance: Hyperacusis, misophonia, phonophobia. *ITHS News Letter 2*, 5–7. http://www.hazell.plus.com/iths/papers1/DST_NL2_PJMJ.pdf

Jastreboff, P. J., & Jastreboff, M. M. (2014). Treatments for decreased sound tolerance (hyperacusis and misophonia). In *Seminars in hearing* (Vol. 35, pp. 105–120). Thieme Medical Publishers. http://doi.org/10.1055/s-0034-1372527

Johnson, P. L., Webber, T. A., Wu, M. S., Lewin, A. B., Murphy, T. K., & Storch, E. A. (2013). When selective audiovisual stimuli become unbearable: A case series on pediatric misophonia. *Neuropsychiatry 3*, 569–575. doi: 10.2217/npy.13.70

Kilner, J. M., & Lemon, R. N. (2013). What we know currently about mirror neurons. *Current Biology* : CB, 23(23), R1057–R1062. https://doi.org/10.1016/j.cub.2013.10.051

Kluckow, H., Telfer, J., & Abraham, S. (2014). Should we screen for misophonia in patients with eating disorders? A report of three cases. *International Journal of Eating Disorders, 47*, 558–561. https://onlinelibrary.wiley.com/doi/10.1002/eat.22245

Kumar, S., Tansley-Hancock, O., Sedley, W., Winston, J. S., Callaghan, M. F., Allen, M., Cope, T. E., Gander, P. E,. Bamiou, D., & Griffiths, T. D. (2017). The brain basis for misophonia. *Current Biology, 27*(4), 527–533. https://www.sciencedirect.com/science/article/pii/S0960982216315305?via%3Dihub

Kumar, S., Dheerendra, P., Erfanian, M., Benzaquén, E., Sedley, W., Gander, P. E., Lad, M., Bamiou, D. E., & Griffiths, T. D. (2021). The Motor Basis for Misophonia. *The*

Journal of neuroscience : the official journal of the Society for Neuroscience, 41(26), 5762–5770. https://doi.org/10.1523/JNEUROSCI.0261-21.2021

LeDoux, J. (2003). The emotional brain, fear, and the amygdala. *Cellular and Molecular Neurobiology, 23*(4-5), 727–738.

LeDoux J. E. (2012). Rethinking the emotional brain. *Neuron, 73*(4), 653–676. https://doi.org/10.1016/j.neuron.2012.02.004

LeDoux, J. (2015). *Anxious: Using the brain to understand and treat fear and anxiety.* Penguin Books.

LeDoux, J. E., & Brown, R. (2017). A higher-order theory of emotional consciousness. *Proceedings of the National Academy of Sciences of the United States of America, 114*(11), E2016–E2025. https://doi.org/10.1073/pnas.1619316114

Low, P. (2020). Overview of the autonomic nervous system. *The Merck Manual.* https://www.merckmanuals.com/home/brain,-spinal-cord,-and-nerve disorders/autonomic-nervous-system-disorders/overview-of-the-autonomic-nervous-system

Mailloux, Z., & Smith Roley, S. (2013). *Sensory integration development and early signs of difficulties.* Pathways.org. https://pathways.org/topics-of-development/sensory/

The Merck Manual's Editorial Staff. (2020). *Obsessive-compulsive personality disorder.* Merck Manual. https://www.merckmanuals.com/home/quick-facts-mental-health-disorders/personality-disorders/obsessive-compulsive-personality-disorder-ocpd?query=ocpd

Miller, L., Nielsen, D. M., Schoen, S. A., & Brett-Green, B. A. (2009). Perspectives on sensory processing disorder: A call for translational research. *Frontiers in Integrative Neuroscience.* https://doi.org/10.3389/neuro.07.022.2009

National Institute of Mental Health. (2014). *Tinnitus.* National Institute on Deafness and Other Communication Disorders. https://www.nidcd.nih.gov/health/tinnitus#

National Institute of Mental Health. (2018). *Autism spectrum disorder.* National Institutes of Health. https://www.nimh.nih.gov/health/topics/autism-spectrum-disorders-asd/index.shtml

Neal, M., & Cavanna, A. E., (2012). P3 Selective sound sensitivity syndrome (misophonia) in a patient with Tourette syndrome. *Journal of Neurology, Neurosurgery & Psychiatry, 83,* e1. https://doi.org/10.1136/jnnp-2012-303538.20

Phillips, K. A, & Stein, D. J. (2018). Obsessive-Compulsive Disorder (OCD). *Merck Manual.* https://www.merckmanuals.com/professional/psychiatric-disorders/obsessive-compulsive-and-related-disorders/obsessive-compulsive-disorder-ocd

Pizzi, W. J. (2004). Nature via nurture: Genes, experience, and what makes us human. *Journal of Undergraduate Neuroscience Education, 2*(2), R10–R11.

Rankin, C. H., Abrams, T., Barry, R. J., Bhatnagar, S., Clayton, D. F., Colombo, J., Coppola, G., Geyer, M. A., Glanzman, D. L., Marsland, S., McSweeney, F. K., Wilson, D. A., Wu, C. F., & Thompson, R. F. (2009). Habituation revisited: An updated and revised description of the behavioral characteristics of habituation.

Neurobiology of Learning and Memory, 92(2), 135–138. https://doi.org/10.1016/j.nlm.2008.09.012

Schröder, A. E., Vulink, N. C., van Loon, A. J., & Denys, D. A. (2017). Cognitive behavioral therapy is effective in misophonia: An open trial. *Journal of Affective Disorders, 217,* 289–294. https://doi.org/10.1016/j.jad.2017.04.017

Schröder, A., van Wingen, Eijsker, N., San Giorgi, R., Vulink, N.C., Turbyne, C., & Densys, D. (2019). Misophonia is associated with altered brain activity in the auditory cortex and salience network. Scientific Reports, 9. https://www.nature.com/articles/s41598-019-44084-8

Schröder, A., Denys, D., & Vulink, N. (2013). Misophonia: Diagnostic criteria for a new psychiatric disorder. *PLOS One, 8*(1): e54706. https://doi.org/10.1371/journal.pone.0054706

Shadish, W. R., & Baldwin, S. A. (2003). Meta-analysis of MFT interventions. *Journal of Marital and Family Therapy, 29*(4), 547–570. https://onlinelibrary.wiley.com/doi/epdf/10.1111/j.1752-0606.2003.tb01694.x

Shanker, S., & Barker, T. (2017). *Self-reg: How to help your child (and you) break the stress cycle and successfully engage with life.* Penguin Books.

Tomaino, C. (2019, April 23) Rhythm, music and movement for Parkinson's: Dr. An interview with Concetta Tomaino. Biodex Medical Systems. https://www.biodex.com/physical-medicine/blog/rhythm-music-and-movement-parkinson%E2%80%99s-dr-interview-concetta-tomaino

University of San Francisco. (n.d). *Hyperacusis treatments.*
    https://www.ucsfhealth.org/conditions/hyperacusis/treatm
    ent#:~:text=Retraining%20therapy%20consists%20of%2
    0counseling,sound%20in%20a%20positive%20manner

Webber, T. A., Johnson, P. L., & Storch, E. A. (2014). Pediatric
    misophonia with comorbid obsessive–compulsive
    spectrum disorders. *General Hospital Psychiatry, 36,*
    231-e1-231.e2. doi:

Printed in Great Britain
by Amazon

43085747R00076